# What to do when you can't do fractions, decimals and percentages

By
Steve Chinn

Egon Publishers Ltd

What to do when you can't do fractions, decimals and percentages

First published 2009

Egon Publishers Ltd
618 Leeds Road, Outwood
Wakefield WF1 2LT

Tel/FAX: 01924 871697
www.egon.co.uk
information@egon.co.uk

ISBN: 978 1904160 97 7

There are 5 books in this series :-

What to do when you can't tell the time
What to do when you can't add and subtract
What to do when you can't multiply and divide
What to do when you can't do the times tables
What to do when you can't do fractions, decimals and percentages

Typeset by Omega Cottage DTP and Web Design
Tingley, Wakefield

## About this book

Fractions often create great anxiety and resistance in people. Decimals, when presented as money cause less anxiety. Percentages are often better understood, but interest rates offered in shops or by banks are often misinterpreted or underestimated.

The main objective of this book is to demystify fractions and then link all three topics together to enhance the reader's understanding of each separate topic.

Fractions are introduced quite early in school maths, perhaps before pupils are ready for them. Or maybe educators underestimate the confusion that the rules of fractions can cause. Fractions seem to demand a completely new set of rules, rules that challenge previous understanding. They also come with a bad reputation for causing anxiety and confusion. Many adults pass on their anxieties to children.

This book tries to explain why fractions cause learning problems and how these problems can be overcome. It addresses everyday uses of fractions, decimals and percentages so that the reader is better prepared to understand and deal with them.

This book explains how to understand the changes needed to work with fractions, decimals and percentages. It also explains how confusion may be caused by these new topics. It is not necessarily the learner's fault that fractions, decimals and percentages are perceived as irrational and impossible.

One of the reasons for the confusion that often surrounds fractions, decimals and percentages is that all three disguise their dependence on division. Division is not a well understood operation! Also, division causes far more anxiety than the other three operations, addition, subtraction and multiplication.

This book tries to explain why fractions, decimals and percentages do what they do and how they are linked. It is not so much a workbook, but more of a 'why it works' and 'why it may not work' book. It looks at why these topics are challenging and provides learner-friendly ways of dealing with those challenges.

The reason behind the linking of fractions, decimals and percentages in this book is to try and use each topic to strengthen your understanding of the other topics. The book also uses different images and different explanations for topics so that there are extra opportunities to find images and explanations that help everyone. A particular explanation on its own may not make everything clear, but it might add a vital piece of clarity to help with the understanding you gain from another explanation.

I think that decimals and percentages were introduced to make life easier by offering an alternative to fractions, in fact to offer ways to actually avoid fractions. Both these ways of presenting parts of whole numbers 'hide' the fact that they are really fractions by hiding the denominator, the bottom number of a fraction (for example the 3 in $\frac{2}{3}$ is the denominator). This means we only see one number instead of the two we use in fractions. They also remove the line, or division symbol. For example, $\frac{3}{4}$ becomes 75% or 0.75.

Similarly, the metric system of measurements uses the pre-fixes, 'centi' (1/100) and 'milli' (1/1000) to avoid the use of fractions and decimals. So, for example, $\frac{1}{4}$ metre becomes 250 mm.

**Note: The fractions used in everyday life are a half and a quarter and, occasionally, a third. Also everyday life does not require you to add, subtract, multiply and divide fractions. Thus, much of the sections on these topics in this book are primarily relevant to what is taught in schools.**

## Introduction

The fractions we meet in everyday life are the half and the quarter. People tend to deal better with these two fractions when they are presented as words rather than as symbols, $\frac{1}{2}$ and $\frac{1}{4}$. In other words, they understand the concept of half and quarter until maths symbols are introduced.

We then have decimals, fractions and percentages as alternative ways of expressing values less than one. The most common example of fractions in everyday life is money, for example, one pence is £0.01. We see percentages at sale time in shops, for example, '50% off', or when we are taking out a loan when interest rates are given as a percentage. The three forms are closely linked.

## Three ways of writing the same thing

Fractions, decimals and percentages are all ways of dealing with values less than 1 (though all three can also deal with values greater than 1).

The common, everyday equivalent examples of this inter-relationship are:

|  | Fraction | Decimal | Percentage |
|---|---|---|---|
| Half | $\frac{1}{2}$ | 0.5 | 50% |
| Quarter | $\frac{1}{4}$ | 0.25 | 25% |
| Tenth | $\frac{1}{10}$ | 0.1 | 10% |
| Hundredth | $\frac{1}{100}$ | 0.01 | 1% |

The parallels would be even closer if we added in an extra zero for the decimal values 0.5 and 0.1. The extra zero has no meaning in terms of the value of the decimal. In fact, if you key 0.50 into most calculators it will change it to 0.5.

The extra zero is used with money, so half a pound, 50p, is written as £0.50.

|  | Fraction | Decimal | Percentage |
|---|---|---|---|
| Half | $\frac{1}{2}$ | 0.50 | 50% |
| Quarter | $\frac{1}{4}$ | 0.25 | 25% |
| Tenth | $\frac{1}{10}$ | 0.10 | 10% |
| Hundredth | $\frac{1}{100}$ | 0.01 | 1% |

A 10 x 10 square, 100 small squares, can give us a picture of all of these key values.
The shaded squares represent the values.

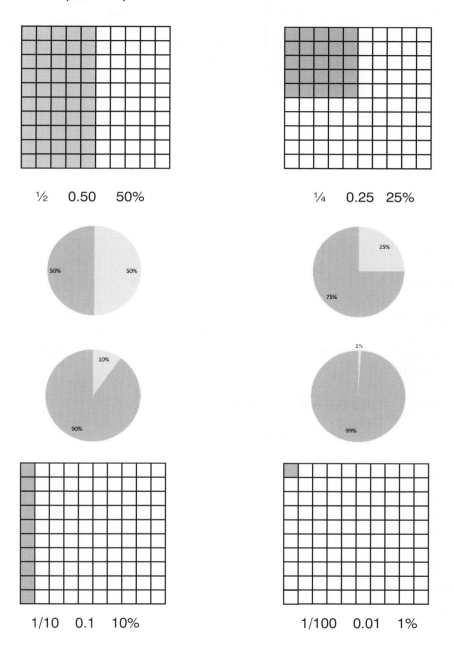

½    0.50    50%          ¼    0.25    25%

1/10    0.1    10%          1/100    0.01    1%

Not all images appeal to all learners. An alternative image that could be used is coins.

The £1 is used as the whole.

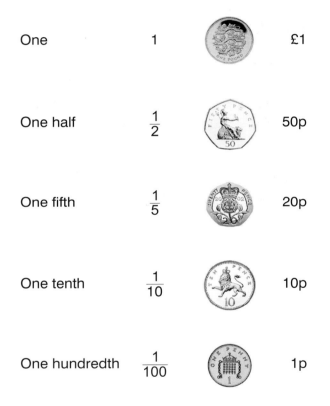

| | | | |
|---|---|---|---|
| One | 1 | | £1 |
| One half | $\frac{1}{2}$ | | 50p |
| One fifth | $\frac{1}{5}$ | | 20p |
| One tenth | $\frac{1}{10}$ | | 10p |
| One hundredth | $\frac{1}{100}$ | | 1p |

Coins have the benefit of being familiar. However, one key difference to the 100 squares image is that the coins are not proportional in size to the values they represent, for example, the £1 coin is not ten times bigger than the 10p coin.

Visual images are quite individual in their appeal and effectiveness. It is good if you can find the 'pictures' that work for you.

**Things to check #1. The decimal point**

The decimal point as used in the UK is, of course, identical to a full stop.

So, if I am writing about decimals and I end a sentence with a decimal number, you will see two dots, for example,

'Half a pound (£1) is written as £0.50.'

The dot between 0 and 5 is the decimal point. The dot after 0.50 is the full stop. The meaning of the dot  .  depends on the context in which it is used.

In some European countries the decimal point is replaced by a comma, for example,  €13,5 (13 Euro, 50 cents).

## Fractions

You can learn almost everything you need to know about doing fractions by using halves and quarters as examples. If you have some understanding of what a half and a quarter mean and represent then that understanding can be the base for your learning.

What works for a half and a quarter works for any fraction, so if you can recall what you learned for a half and quarter it will help you remember the procedures for all fractions. We are trying to use what you already know to understand more about fractions.

Some early work with fractions is much easier when you use only the words. As soon as symbols are introduced, the misunderstandings begin.

Why do we write one half as $\frac{1}{2}$ ?

The reason is in how we halve something. When we want to divide something into two halves we divide it into two equal parts. The key word is divide.

The symbol for a half, $\frac{1}{2}$ hides a division sign.

We start with a division symbol $\frac{\bullet}{\bullet}$

When we put in the 1 and the 2 onto a division sign, the dots are replaced and ÷ becomes $\frac{1}{2}$.

So, in maths, $\frac{1}{2}$ actually means 1 divided by 2, which is what a half is.

One of the reasons people find fractions challenging is that they forget that fractions are made up from two numbers, one of which is divided by the other.

When we say 'two' we simply mean 2, a number, a quantity, but

when we say 'half' it means 1 divided by 2,  1 ÷ 2

or for 'three quarters' means 3 divided by 4,  3 ÷ 4

So the division means that fractions are more complicated that ordinary numbers, but if we remember that the division is there then we are less likely to make mistakes.

## Everyday halves

Because the word 'half' is in common use, it is not always used in an accurate mathematical sense.

For example, it is close to impossible to cut a pizza or an apple into two mathematically equal halves. You can cut them into two approximately sized portions, but they are not halves in a mathematical sense of total equality.

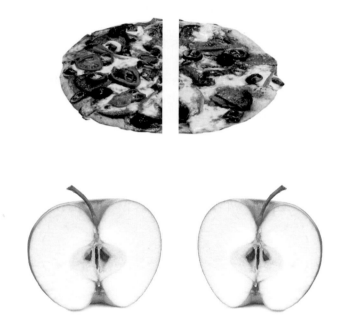

When my son was a teenager he always asked for 'the bigger half'. Again not a mathematical possibility, but understandable!

On long drives, his sister would ask, 'Are we half way there yet?' She could have meant half way in journey time, or half way in journey distance. I could answer the latter meaning reasonably accurately, but the time version would be based on an estimate, due to traffic conditions and so forth.

If someone owns 51% of a business, they have just over half of it and should, therefore have control. 51% is close to a half, but is not exactly a half. The extra 1% can mean a lot in some circumstances. When people say, 'See you in half an hour' they do not always turn up in exactly 30 minutes.

So, in everyday life, 'half' is often used as an estimate.

In maths, it has to be precise!

**Things to check #2. Vocabulary**

A fraction is made up from a horizontal line, a number above the line (sometimes called, logically, the 'top' number) and a number below the line (sometimes called the 'bottom' number).

The mathematical vocabulary for these two numbers are the **numerator** and the **denominator**.

The denominator (bottom) tells us the name ('nom' is French for name and is a part of the word de**nom**inator) of the fraction, for example, **third** or **tenth**.

The numerator (top) tells us the number of parts we have of that particular name fraction, for example, two thirds or seven tenths. Perhaps it should have been called 'numberator'.

$$\frac{2}{3} \quad \begin{array}{l} \text{numerator} \\ \text{denominator} \end{array}$$

Once again it is easier to understand if we say the fractions rather than write them in symbols.

For example, if we ask, 'What is five ninths plus two ninths?' the answer is logically 'seven ninths'.

**Different 'forms' or 'names' of fractions, known as *equivalent* (equal in value) fractions**

Once again words make the understanding easier than the symbols and numbers, but simply using the word 'half' may hide some variations on that idea. For example, we use 'half' to describe:

Half an hour, which is thirty minutes out of sixty minutes.

Half a £, which is fifty pence out of one hundred pence.

Half a kilogram, which is five hundred grams out of one thousand grams.

Half a mile, which is eight hundred and eighty yards out of one thousand, seven hundred and sixty yards.

This single word 'half' can be presented in many ways as soon as we start to use numbers.

There are lots of ways to write a half with numbers.

The most common way is, of course,    $\frac{1}{2}$    or    $\frac{1}{2}$

When we write 'half an hour', which is 30 minutes out of 60 minutes, we write the fraction as:

$$\frac{30}{60}$$

We write 'half a litre', which is 500 ml out of 1000 ml as:    $\frac{500}{1000}$

'Half a year', which is 6 months out of 12 months as:  $\dfrac{6}{12}$

'Half a century', which is 50 out of 100 as:  $\dfrac{50}{100}$

**The pattern for all versions of a half**

There is a pattern in these examples, and patterns help learning.

The pattern is that in each of these numerical versions of a half, the top number is half the value of the bottom number.

Using mathematical vocabulary, to make an equivalent version of a half, $\frac{1}{2}$ the numerator must be half the value of the denominator.

Try completing these halves by writing in the appropriate bottom (denominator) number. The first one is done for you.

$$\frac{2}{4} \quad \frac{5}{\square} \quad \frac{12}{\square} \quad \frac{25}{\square} \quad \frac{100}{\square} \quad \frac{500}{\square}$$

Try completing these halves by writing in the appropriate top (numerator) number. The first one is done for you.

$$\frac{3}{6} \quad \frac{\square}{14} \quad \frac{\square}{30} \quad \frac{\square}{48} \quad \frac{\square}{2000}$$

It may help to have some visual images of a half as equivalent fractions.

Try creating this visual image, if you take a sheet of paper and fold it and shade it as in the diagrams.

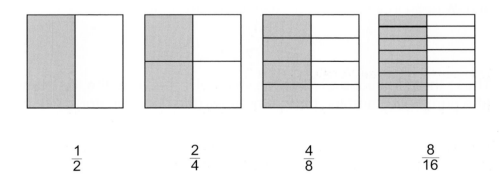

$$\frac{1}{2} \qquad \frac{2}{4} \qquad \frac{4}{8} \qquad \frac{8}{16}$$

When a half is written in these different ways, the fractions are called **equivalent fractions.** Equivalent means that the fractions are identical to each other in value, even if they use different numbers.

Each equivalent fraction has a different name, a different denominator.

The diagrams above show a half as:

one half          two quarters          four eighths          eight sixteenths

Being able to rename fractions, change the denominator, and thus make equivalent fractions is a **key skill** when working with fractions.

Equivalent fractions for a half may not look like $\frac{1}{2}$, but they are still a half.

## Multiplying by one

When children learn the times table facts they learn that the 1x table facts are easy because the answers are the same (value) as the number multiplied by 1. For example,

$$\textbf{3 x 1 = 3}$$
$$\textbf{8 x 1 = 8}$$

Equivalent fractions are made by multiplying a fraction by 1, but the 1 is now used in the form of a fraction, for example:

$$\frac{2}{2} \quad \text{or} \quad \frac{7}{7} \quad \text{or} \quad \frac{100}{100}$$

These three fractions all have the value of 1, because the top number (the numerator) and the bottom number (the denominator) have the same value, they are the same numbers.

2 and 2          7 and 7          100 and 100

So, because a fraction was multiplied by 1, it has the same value, but it will look different because it is using different numbers.

For example, a half $\frac{1}{2}$ when multiplied by $\frac{7}{7}$ becomes $\frac{7}{14}$, which is still a half.

A half when multiplied by $\frac{100}{100}$ becomes $\frac{100}{200}$ which is still a half.

16

**Examples for practicing equivalent fractions**

Now try making some equivalents for fractions other than a half.

Make two (different) equivalent fractions for each fraction below:
One example is done for you.

1) $\dfrac{3}{5}$  $\dfrac{\boxed{\phantom{00}}}{\boxed{\phantom{00}}}$

2) $\dfrac{5}{6}$  $\dfrac{\boxed{50}}{\boxed{60}}$

3) $\dfrac{7}{8}$  $\dfrac{\boxed{\phantom{00}}}{\boxed{\phantom{00}}}$

4) $\dfrac{11}{20}$  $\dfrac{\boxed{\phantom{00}}}{\boxed{\phantom{00}}}$

5) $\dfrac{5}{9}$  $\dfrac{\boxed{\phantom{00}}}{\boxed{\phantom{00}}}$

6) $\dfrac{10}{13}$  $\dfrac{\boxed{\phantom{00}}}{\boxed{\phantom{00}}}$

**Adding and subtracting fractions: part 1**

In school maths you have to know how to add and subtract fractions. In everyday life the most likely example is when you have to add and subtract half hours and quarter hours.

Let's start with something we know:

A half plus a half equals (or makes) one (whole).

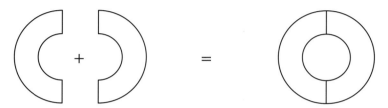

Again, as my colleague, Richard Ashcroft says, 'In maths the words are easier than the numbers'. Once we put 'a half plus a half' into symbols it looks more complicated;

$$\frac{1}{2} \ + \ \frac{1}{2} \ = \ 1$$

This number statement hides some rules, one of which is really quite strange and, at first sight, illogical.

When we deal with whole numbers, 'add' means put together the numbers. For example,

$$1 + 1 = 2$$

But we are working with fractions and things are not quite that straightforward.

It is when we write the fractions as symbols that they can start to confuse. Again, the symbols below provide a summary of the words,

'half plus a half equals 1'

$$\frac{1}{2} \ + \ \frac{1}{2} \ = \ 1$$

There is an intermediate step we should write in when we use symbols. This intermediate step introduces a process that can be confusing.

**Note:** When adding fractions we only add the top numbers, in this example, the 1's. We do not add the bottom numbers, the 2's.

When working with fractions, the addition (or subtraction) sign only acts on the top numbers, the numerators.

$$\frac{1}{2} \ + \ \frac{1}{2} \ = \ \frac{2}{2} \ = \ 1$$

$$\frac{3}{4} \ - \ \frac{1}{4} \ = \ \frac{2}{4}$$

The 2 and 4 used as the bottom numbers (**denominators**) of the fractions, identify or name the fraction. It may help you to remember this if you can see 'nom' in the word denominator. 'Nom' is French for name (as in 'nom de plume', which means 'pen name'). The 2 tells us that the fraction is a half.

This example of a half plus a half helps us to understand how the symbols do what the words do:

'**One** half plus **one** half equals **two** halves.'

The halves remain halves. We add one half to one half to get two halves. We are adding two things (or quantities) with the same name, so the name, half, doesn't change, but the number of halves does.

So, to repeat the rule, we do not add the denominator, the bottom numbers, the 2's. The + and − signs only apply to the top numbers (the numerators). This rule applies to both subtraction and addition of fractions.

**Note:**

The two in $\frac{1}{2}$ tells us that the name of this fraction is a half.

The four in $\frac{1}{4}$ tells us that the name of this fraction is a quarter.

The same is true for adding all fractions with the same name, for example, with quarters:

'One **quarter** plus one **quarter** equals two **quarters**.'

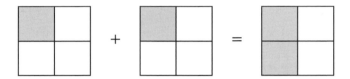

The reverse operation of subtraction would be:

'Two **quarters** minus one **quarter** equals one **quarter**.'

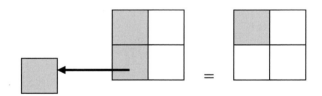

It may be easier to understand these sums if you **say** the sum rather than if you **write it in symbols**. For example, the words:

'Two **sevenths** plus three **sevenths** equals five **sevenths**.'

may be easier to understand than the numbers:

$$\frac{2}{7} \quad + \quad \frac{3}{7} \quad = \quad \frac{5}{7}$$

The subtraction is the reverse of the addition. Again, the denominators have to be the same. The subtraction sign only operates on the top number (the numerator):

'Five **sevenths** minus three **sevenths** equals two **sevenths**'.

Again the words make the process more logical.

$$\frac{5}{7} - \frac{3}{7} = \frac{2}{7}$$

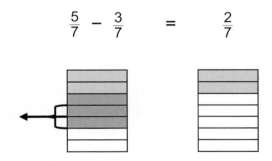

We meet this example of adding same name fractions when we talk about time.

A quarter of an hour plus a quarter of an hour makes two quarters of an hour which we convert to the equivalent fraction, half an hour.

**Things to check #3. The language of fractions**

The language and vocabulary of a topic can help, or hinder, our learning. Ideally the language and vocabulary should follow a pattern. Sadly this is not always the case with mathematics.

The most common fractions, half, third and quarter have names which are exceptions to the rule for naming other fractions. So, in starting with these fractions we are not building a pattern of words. The next fractions in the sequence are better and are regular:

$$\text{fifth, } \frac{1}{5} \quad \text{sixth, } \frac{1}{6} \quad \text{seventh, } \frac{1}{7} \quad \text{eighth, } \frac{1}{8} \quad \text{ninth, } \frac{1}{9} \quad \text{and so on.}$$

There could also be some extra confusion around 'third' since this word is also used to indicate order as in, 'I came third in that race.'

Using fraction names may help you to understand why fractions have to have the same name to be added or subtracted.

For example, it makes sense to add two ninths to five ninths to make seven ninths, whereas the word version of adding fractions with different names makes the process seem impossible whilst the fractions are in those forms, for example:

> 'Add two sevenths to four ninths' does not lead you to a verbally logical next step.

## Adding fractions: part 2

In part 1, I explained about the bottom number in a fraction being the name of the fraction the denominator. We only added fractions with the same name, the same denominator.

So what happens if the names, the denominators, are not the same?

If we go back to halves and quarters, where we know what the answer should be, we should be able to get a better understanding of the next step in adding and subtracting fractions.

What happens when we add one half to one quarter? We know the answer is three quarters. So what is the explanation?

$$\frac{1}{2} \; + \; \frac{1}{4} \; = \; \frac{3}{4}$$

The rule is:

**Fractions can only be added mathematically when they have the same name, a 'common denominator'.**

For example, we cannot add a half to a quarter without changing the half to its equivalent fraction 'two quarters'.

So, if the fractions do not have the same name, one or both of the fractions have to be renamed. They have to be changed to equivalent fractions with the same name.

**Note:** Equivalent fractions are fractions with the same value, but with a different denominator and, as a consequence on the change to the denominator, a different numerator.

So with ¼ and ½ the denominators are not the same. In this example, we can change the half, so that one half is renamed as two quarters. Think of a clock and time, one half hour is the same as two quarter hours.

$$\frac{1}{2} = \frac{2}{4}$$

The two fractions have the same value, one half.  They just look different when written in numbers because they use different (but related) numbers.

We looked at many different 'forms' (equivalents) of a half on pages 13-16. What made them all one half was the relationship between the numerator and the denominator.

The numerator was always one half of the value of the denominator.

$\frac{2}{4}$  fits into this pattern.  $\frac{2}{4}$ is an equivalent fraction to $\frac{1}{2}$.

The way this works mathematically is that both numbers, the top and the bottom numbers, in the fraction that we want to rename are multiplied by the same number, in this case 2.

So, we multiply the numerator by 2 and we multiply the denominator by 2.

$$\frac{1}{2} \times \frac{2}{2} = \frac{2}{4}$$

**Note:** We only use one multiplication sign, one x, even though we are doing two multiplications. It may not make sense, and is different to how we use the + and − symbols, but that is the convention, and we are stuck with it!

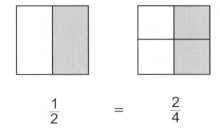

$$\frac{1}{2} \qquad = \qquad \frac{2}{4}$$

The reason why we multiply both the denominator and the numerator is that we are renaming the fraction, not changing its value. This means that what we do to the top number (multiply or divide), the numerator, we must also do to the bottom number, the denominator (multiply or divide).

If we are adding a half, then we must add a half, even if it is now an equivalent version of a half, otherwise the question is not the same. Renaming a fraction does not change its value, only the way it looks in terms of its numerator and denominator.

Multiplying by $\frac{2}{2}$ is multiplying by 1, since $\frac{2}{2}$ is 1 and multiplying by 1 does not change the value, even though it changes the 'look' of the fraction.

Now our quarter and our half have the same name, the same denominator, and we can add them:

$$\frac{1}{2} \ + \ \frac{2}{4} \ = \ \frac{3}{4}$$

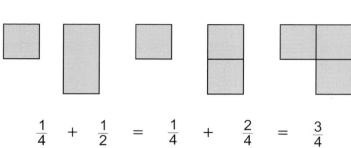

$$\frac{1}{4} \ + \ \frac{1}{2} \ = \ \frac{1}{4} \ + \ \frac{2}{4} \ = \ \frac{3}{4}$$

Since we meet this addition in everyday experiences of time, we know the answer is correct. This example is used because it demonstrates the way we work out an answer when the denominators are different. The method is illustrative of how to do many other problems involving the addition (and subtraction) of fractions.

**Fractions which add to make 1**

It is useful to know how two fractions can add up to make 1. What are the characteristics of these fractions?

As ever, let's start with the fractions we know best, half and quarter.

$$\frac{1}{2} + \frac{1}{2} = \frac{2}{2} = 1$$

$$\frac{3}{4} + \frac{1}{4} = \frac{4}{4} = 1$$

$$\frac{1}{4} + \frac{1}{4} + \frac{1}{4} + \frac{1}{4} = \frac{4}{4} = 1$$

Now let's strengthen the pattern by working with some other fractions:

$$\frac{7}{10} + \frac{3}{10} = \frac{10}{10} = 1$$

$$\frac{12}{25} + \frac{13}{25} = \frac{25}{25} = 1$$

In order for two (or more) fractions to add up to make 1, the top numbers (numerators) must add up to the same value as the (common) denominator (bottom number). In the two examples above the top numbers have to add to 10 for the first example and 25 for the second example.

## Subtraction of fractions

The procedures for subtraction are the same as those for addition. The only difference is that the numerators (top numbers) are subtracted instead of added.

For example,
$$\frac{7}{11} - \frac{3}{11} = \frac{4}{11}$$

$$\frac{5}{9} - \frac{1}{9} = \frac{4}{9}$$

## Creating equivalent fractions

When a number is multiplied by 1, its value stays the same.

To rename a fraction we multiply by 1, but we use a fraction version of 1. In our changing a half to two quarters example we multiply by $\frac{2}{2}$ (which is a fraction version of 1).

Fraction versions of 1 have the same value number for the denominator and the numerator.

Some other examples of renaming $\frac{1}{2}$ (see also pages 13-16).

$$\frac{1}{2} \times \frac{5}{5} = \frac{5}{10} \qquad \frac{1}{2} \times \frac{10}{10} = \frac{10}{20} \qquad \frac{1}{2} \times \frac{25}{25} = \frac{25}{50} \qquad \frac{1}{2} \times \frac{50}{50} = \frac{50}{100}$$

## Practice

a) $\dfrac{1}{2} \times \dfrac{4}{4} = \dfrac{\Box}{\Box}$

b) $\dfrac{1}{3} \times \dfrac{5}{5} = \dfrac{\Box}{\Box}$

c) $\dfrac{2}{3} \times \dfrac{10}{10} = \dfrac{\Box}{\Box}$

d) $\dfrac{5}{8} \times \dfrac{2}{2} = \dfrac{\Box}{\Box}$

e) $\dfrac{10}{11} \times \dfrac{5}{5} = \dfrac{\Box}{\Box}$

f) $\dfrac{3}{13} \times \dfrac{20}{20} = \dfrac{\Box}{\Box}$

g) $\dfrac{10}{11} \times \dfrac{7}{\Box} = \dfrac{\Box}{\Box}$

h) $\dfrac{5}{9} \times \dfrac{2}{\Box} = \dfrac{\Box}{\Box}$

i) $\dfrac{3}{10} \times \dfrac{\Box}{5} = \dfrac{\Box}{\Box}$

**Answers:**

g) 7/7 = 70/77            h) 2/2 = 10/18            i) 5/5 = 15/50

d) 10/16                  e) 50/55                  f) 60/260

a) 4/8                    b) 5/15                   c) 20/30

## Cancelling and the simplest form

This is the reverse process of renaming as described above.

The simplest form of a half is $\frac{1}{2}$.

All the other forms of a half can be reduced down to this simplest form by 'cancelling'.

So, to rename $\frac{1}{2}$ as tenths, we multiplied the fraction by $\frac{5}{5}$ which is a form of 1.

This gave us a half that was written as $\frac{1}{2} \times \frac{5}{5} = \frac{5}{10}$

To return to the simplest form, $\frac{1}{2}$ we divide by $\frac{5}{5}$ (we reverse the process).

This means that we divide the top number, the numerator, by 5 and also the bottom number, the denominator, by 5.

This is also known as 'cancelling'. In order to cancel you have to recognise what numbers divide into the numbers of the fraction. These numbers are called 'factors'.

To explain what a factor is, think of a times table fact, such as:

$$5 \times 6 = 30$$

30 is the product of 5 and 6

5 and 6 are the **factors** of 30

Factors are numbers that divide, exactly, into another number, in this example 30.

Factors could be 'seen' as the reverse of times table facts.

The times table version of a fact is, for example,     $4 \times 5 = 20$

The factor version is:                                $20 = 4 \times 5$


## Things to check #4

If you are unable to remember the factors then cancelling to the simplest form may be difficult. There are a couple of useful tests/comparisons you can make for cancelling by 2, by 5 and by 9.

'2'    Any even number is divisible by 2. Even numbers end in (have their unit digit as) 0, 2, 4, 6, 8.
       This also deals with 4 and 8 if you can divide by 2 a second or a third time.

'3'    If a number is divisible by 3 the digits in the number will add up to 3, 6 or 9, (even if this takes more than one step).

'5'    Any number that ends in 0 or 5 is divisible by 5.

'9'    If all the digits that make a number add up to 9, then the number is divisible by 9.

       For example:          874512

                        $8+7+4+5+1+2 = 27$

                             $2+7 = 9$

                        $874512 \div 9 = 97168$

'10'  Any number that ends in 0 is divisible by 10.

## Things to check # 5

Another way to find factors for calculating equivalent fractions and for cancelling down to the simplest form is to use the times table square.

For example, to find equivalent fractions for 3/7, look down the 3 and the 7 columns in the times table square. Each pair of numbers across makes a new equivalent fraction. So, reading down the pairs, we have:

$$\frac{3}{7} \qquad \frac{6}{14} \qquad \frac{9}{21} \qquad \frac{12}{28} \qquad \frac{15}{35}$$

$$\frac{18}{42} \qquad \frac{21}{49} \qquad \frac{24}{56} \qquad \frac{27}{63} \qquad \frac{30}{70}$$

|    | 0 | 1 | 2 | 3 | 4 | 5 | 6 | 7 | 8 | 9 | 10 |
|----|---|---|---|---|---|---|---|---|---|---|----|
| 0  | 0 | 0 | 0 | 0 | 0 | 0 | 0 | 0 | 0 | 0 | 0 |
| 1  | 0 | 1 | 2 | 3 | 4 | 5 | 6 | 7 | 8 | 9 | 10 |
| 2  | 0 | 2 | 4 | 6 | 8 | 10 | 12 | 14 | 16 | 18 | 20 |
| 3  | 0 | 3 | 6 | 9 | 12 | 15 | 18 | 21 | 24 | 27 | 30 |
| 4  | 0 | 4 | 8 | 12 | 16 | 20 | 24 | 28 | 32 | 36 | 40 |
| 5  | 0 | 5 | 10 | 15 | 20 | 25 | 30 | 35 | 40 | 45 | 50 |
| 6  | 0 | 6 | 12 | 18 | 24 | 30 | 36 | 42 | 48 | 54 | 60 |
| 7  | 0 | 7 | 14 | 21 | 28 | 35 | 42 | 49 | 56 | 63 | 70 |
| 8  | 0 | 8 | 16 | 24 | 32 | 40 | 48 | 56 | 64 | 72 | 80 |
| 9  | 0 | 9 | 18 | 27 | 36 | 45 | 54 | 63 | 72 | 81 | 90 |
| 10 | 0 | 10 | 20 | 30 | 40 | 50 | 60 | 70 | 80 | 90 | 100 |

You would reverse this procedure to find the simplest form. For example, if the fraction was 21/49, find 21 and 49 on the same horizontal line and then track back up the two columns to find 3 and 7 and thus 3/7.

Try finding all the equivalent fractions from the times table square for

$$\frac{1}{2} \qquad \frac{1}{9} \qquad \frac{3}{5}$$

Try finding the simplest form for

a) $\frac{9}{27}$      b) $\frac{8}{72}$      c) $\frac{21}{56}$

Answers for the simplest form questions:

c) $\frac{3}{8}$      b) $\frac{1}{6}$      a) $\frac{1}{3}$

## Adding and subtracting any fractions

**The rule is:** adding and subtracting can only start when the fractions involved have the same denominator, that is the same name: 'a common denominator'.

'Common' in this context means 'in common' or the 'same' denominator.

To achieve this situation we use an arithmetic relationship we used to help reduce the number of times tables basic facts that had to be learned (see *'What to do when you can't learn the times tables'*).

The technical term is **'the commutative property'**.

What this means is that you always get the same answer when you multiply two given numbers irrespective of the order of multiplication.

For example:

$$8 \times 3 = 24 \quad \text{and} \quad 3 \times 8 = 24$$

$$7 \times 9 = 63 \quad \text{and} \quad 9 \times 7 = 63$$

$$2 \times 6 = 12 \quad \text{and} \quad 6 \times 2 = 12$$

$$5 \times 4 = 20 \quad \text{and} \quad 4 \times 5 = 20$$

## Things to check #6

Algebra can help us to generalise and make a rule or formula for any numbers. If we use 'a' to represent the first number and 'b' to represent the second number in these multiplications, then:

$$a \times b = b \times a$$

So, a specific example could have 'a' representing 6 and 'b' representing 4, so a x b becomes 6 x 4 and b x a becomes 4 x 6.

$$6 \times 4 = 4 \times 6$$

Another example could replace 'a' with 5 and 'b' with 10,

so a x b becomes  5 x 10

and b x a becomes  10 x 5

$$5 \times 10 = 10 \times 5$$

**Giving different fractions the same name (common denominator)**

If we want to give two different fractions the same name, we use the commutative fact. For example:

$$\frac{1}{2} \quad \text{and} \quad \frac{1}{5}$$

We take the denominators, 2 and 5, and use the fact that:

$$\text{both} \quad 2 \times 5 \quad \text{and} \quad 5 \times 2 \quad \text{equal} \quad 10.$$

We rename both fractions as tenths. We make the denominator, the bottom number, 10 for both fractions.

So we multiply the first fraction by $\quad \frac{5}{5}$

And we multiply the second fraction by $\quad \frac{2}{2}$

$$\frac{1}{2} \times \frac{5}{5} = \frac{5}{10} \qquad \frac{1}{5} \times \frac{2}{2} = \frac{2}{10}$$

We use the denominator of the second fraction to rename the first fraction, and the denominator of the first fraction to rename the second fraction.

$$\frac{1}{2} \quad = \quad \frac{5}{10} \qquad\qquad \frac{1}{5} \quad = \quad \frac{2}{10}$$

Another example:

$$\frac{2}{3} \quad \text{and} \quad \frac{7}{10}$$

The denominators are 3 and 10.

If we multiply 3 by 10 we get 30,

and if we multiply 10 by 3 we get 30.

The renaming makes both fractions thirtieths:

$$\frac{2}{3} \times \frac{10}{10} = \frac{20}{30} \quad and \quad \frac{7}{10} \times \frac{3}{3} = \frac{21}{30}$$

The renamed fractions can now be added.

## A visual model

We can use the addition of $\frac{1}{2}$ and $\frac{1}{3}$ to illustrate the process of renaming.

Take two squares of paper.

Divide one square into two halves and the other into three thirds.

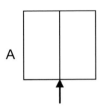
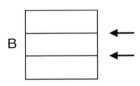

So, paper A has been halved (÷2),
and paper B has been divided into thirds (÷3)

To make both A and B the same, we divide A by 3 and B by 2

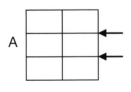
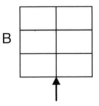

Now A has been divided by 2 and then by 3, divided by 6.

And B has been divided by 3 and then by 2, divided by 6.

When the two processes are finished, then both fractions have had the same divisions and have the same denominators/names.

This illustrates the process of using the denominator of each fraction to create the renaming of the other fraction.

## Things to check #7.  Making denominators common

Once again, algebra can be used to explain the generalisation:

If the two fractions are:    $\dfrac{a}{b}$  and  $\dfrac{c}{d}$

We use d to rename the b fraction:

$$\dfrac{a}{b} \times \dfrac{d}{d}$$    Remember that we rename by    $\dfrac{d}{d}$
multiplying by 1, in this example,

We use b to rename the d fraction:     $\dfrac{c}{d} \times \dfrac{b}{b}$

Both fractions now have the same denominator (bottom number) bd (or db, which is the same when numbers are used instead of letters. For algebra, we do not use the x sign, so  bd and db mean b x d  and d x b).

**Things to check #8.  Lowest common denominator**

When we make a common denominator by multiplying together the two denominators, we may not get the lowest common denominator.

For example, if the fractions are:

$$\frac{1}{4} + \frac{1}{6}$$

Then the multiplying denominators rule gives us:

$$\frac{1}{4} \times \frac{6}{6} + \frac{1}{6} \times \frac{4}{4} \; = \; \frac{6}{24} + \frac{4}{24} \; = \; \frac{10}{24} \; = \; \frac{5}{12}$$

24 is a common denominator for 4 and 6, but it is not the lowest (in number value) common denominator.

Using 24 is not wrong, it is just not the lowest common denominator and therefore not the simplest form of the fraction. (See *'Things to Check #5'* which explains how you can use the times tables square to find equivalent fractions).

**Things to check #9.  The 'Criss-Cross-Times' mnemonic**

A mnemonic is a device to help you remember something
(but rarely explains why it works).

The common denominator method for addition and subtraction of fractions as explained above can be summarised by the 'Criss-Cross-Times' mnemonic.

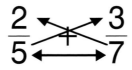

Multiplications take place as directed by the arrows

$$\frac{2 \times 7 + 3 \times 5}{5 \times 7}$$

$$\frac{14 + 15}{35} = \frac{29}{35}$$

## Practice

Try the criss-cross-times method to calculate the answers to these problems.

a) $\frac{3}{4} + \frac{5}{11}$

b) $\frac{4}{7} + \frac{9}{10}$

c) $\frac{2}{7} + \frac{10}{11}$

d) $\frac{4}{5} + \frac{11}{20}$

d) $\frac{11}{20} + \frac{2}{5}$

e) $\frac{5}{11} + \frac{11}{30}$

## Answers:

a) $\frac{53}{44}$

c) $\frac{92}{77}$

b) $\frac{103}{70}$

d) $\frac{135}{100} \left(\frac{27}{20}\right)$

d) $\frac{15}{100} \left(\frac{3}{20}\right)$

e) $\frac{29}{330}$

## Estimating answers

It is good practice to evaluate answers and to estimate what they might be before you start a calculation. It doesn't have to be a close estimate. In this particular application, estimates are used to prevent big mistakes!

Once again a half $\frac{1}{2}$ is useful as a key reference value.

The Fraction Wall shows the relative values of some commonly used fractions.

Half, $\frac{1}{2}$, the key reference value is at the top and the bottom.

| $\frac{1}{2}$ | | | | | | $\frac{1}{2}$ | | | | | |
| $\frac{1}{3}$ | | | | $\frac{1}{3}$ | | | | $\frac{1}{3}$ | | | |
| $\frac{1}{4}$ | | | $\frac{1}{4}$ | | | $\frac{1}{4}$ | | | $\frac{1}{4}$ | | |
| $\frac{1}{5}$ | | $\frac{1}{5}$ | | $\frac{1}{5}$ | | $\frac{1}{5}$ | | $\frac{1}{5}$ | | | |
| $\frac{1}{6}$ | | $\frac{1}{6}$ | | $\frac{1}{6}$ | | $\frac{1}{6}$ | | $\frac{1}{6}$ | | $\frac{1}{6}$ | |
| $\frac{1}{8}$ | $\frac{1}{8}$ | $\frac{1}{8}$ | $\frac{1}{8}$ | $\frac{1}{8}$ | $\frac{1}{8}$ | $\frac{1}{8}$ | $\frac{1}{8}$ | | | | |
| $\frac{1}{10}$ | $\frac{1}{10}$ | $\frac{1}{10}$ | $\frac{1}{10}$ | $\frac{1}{10}$ | $\frac{1}{10}$ | $\frac{1}{10}$ | $\frac{1}{10}$ | $\frac{1}{10}$ | $\frac{1}{10}$ | | |
| $\frac{1}{12}$ | $\frac{1}{12}$ | $\frac{1}{12}$ | $\frac{1}{12}$ | $\frac{1}{12}$ | $\frac{1}{12}$ | $\frac{1}{12}$ | $\frac{1}{12}$ | $\frac{1}{12}$ | $\frac{1}{12}$ | $\frac{1}{12}$ | $\frac{1}{12}$ |
| $\frac{1}{2}$ | | | | | | $\frac{1}{2}$ | | | | | |

**The Fraction Wall**

The wall helps you to compare the value of fractions to the 'size' of a half. For example:

$\frac{5}{12}$ is less than a half and $\frac{7}{12}$ is bigger than a half.

$\frac{3}{5}$ is bigger than $\frac{7}{12}$. Both are bigger than a half.

Paper folding can also be used to compare fraction values.

Cut eight strips of paper, 24 cm long and 5 cm wide.

Strip 1.   Fold in half                                                    2 parts 12 cm each

Strip 2.   Fold in half and then half again
             to give four quarters                          4 parts  6 cm each

Strip 3.   Fold into thirds                                          3 parts  8 cm each

Strip 4.   Fold into thirds and then fold to
             half the thirds, making sixths         6 parts  4 cm each

Strip 5.   Fold into half, then half again and
             then half again, making eighths        8 parts  3 cm each

Strip 6.   Fold into fifths
             (measure out in 4.8 cm sections)       5 parts  4.8 cm each

Strip 7.   Fold in half and then
             fold into fifths (2.4 cm)               10 parts  2.4 cm each

Strip 8.   Fold in half, then thirds,
             then half again, making twelfths       12 parts  2 cm each

The maths behind the folding is:

$$\frac{1}{4} = \frac{1}{2} \times \frac{1}{2}$$

$$\frac{1}{6} = \frac{1}{3} \times \frac{1}{2}$$

$$\frac{1}{8} = \frac{1}{2} \times \frac{1}{2} \times \frac{1}{2}$$

$$\frac{1}{10} = \frac{1}{2} \times \frac{1}{5}$$

$$\frac{1}{12} = \frac{1}{2} \times \frac{1}{3} \times \frac{1}{2}$$

So, if you can't divide by 12, you can use three steps: divide by 2, divide by 2, divide by 3.

When you have made your fraction strips you can use them to show the relative sizes of different fractions and hopefully develop more sense of the values of each fraction. The half strips can always be used as a key comparison for all these demonstrations.

**Adding two fractions: pre-calculation estimate**

Check if either or both of the fractions are greater than or less than a half. This will help you decide if the sum is going to be:

- a lot less than 1
- just under 1
- just over 1
- a lot more than 1

For example: $\dfrac{5}{7} + \dfrac{9}{11}$

Both fractions are comfortably above a half, so the answer will be more than 1, but less than 2.

The actual answer is: $1\dfrac{41}{77}$

Another example: $\dfrac{2}{5} + \dfrac{3}{10}$

Both fractions are less than a half, so the answer will be less than 1.

The actual answer is: $\dfrac{7}{10}$

## Practice for pre-calculation estimates

You do not need to calculate the answer. You have to estimate if the answer will be greater than 1 or less than 1. Tick the box for the answer you chose.

a)    $\frac{3}{10} + \frac{1}{3}$    greater than 1   [   ]      less than 1   [   ]

b)    $\frac{7}{10} + \frac{2}{3}$    greater than 1   [   ]      less than 1   [   ]

c)    $\frac{3}{5} + \frac{4}{7}$    greater than 1   [   ]      less than 1   [   ]

d)    $\frac{1}{5} + \frac{1}{3}$    greater than 1   [   ]      less than 1   [   ]

e)    $\frac{7}{15} + \frac{9}{20}$    greater than 1   [   ]      less than 1   [   ]

Answers:

a) less      b) more      c) more      d) less      e) more

## Multiplying by fractions

We have already gained some experience of multiplying by fractions when we renamed fractions. Unlike addition and subtraction of fractions, the x sign operates on both the top (numerator) and bottom number (denominator).

When we multiplied to rename a fraction we multiplied by a fraction whose value was 1. This did not change the value of the fraction being renamed.

There is a simple sequence here:

- If we multiply by a number whose value is greater than 1, the answer has a bigger value than the number being multiplied.
- If we multiply by 1, the answer has the same value as the number being multiplied.
- If we multiply by a fraction whose value is less than 1, then the answer (the product) will be smaller in value than the number being multiplied.

Once again we can use a half to illustrate the general principle. If we multiply some value by a half it will have a smaller value.

Once again if we use only words the answer is easier than when we use symbols.

For example:    What is a half of twenty-four?

We know the answer is twelve.

The words 'a half of twenty-four' can be translated into maths symbols.

'Half' is $\frac{1}{2}$, remember that $\frac{1}{2}$ hides a division sign.

'of' translates to  $\times$  (multiply)

and, of course, 'twenty-four' translates to 24.

So, 'What is half of twenty-four?' becomes:

$$\frac{1}{2} \times 24$$

and that becomes a two step procedure:

Step 1.                $1 \times 24 \ = \ 24$

Step 2.                $24 \div 2 \ = \ 12$

Another example:

$8 \times \frac{1}{2} = 4$         $8 \times \frac{1}{2} = 4$

If the multiplied number is also less than 1, that too will become smaller.

For example, if we multiply three quarters by one half, the answer is three eighths.

$$\frac{3}{4} \times \frac{1}{2} = \frac{3}{8}$$

Three eighths, $\frac{3}{8}$ is smaller than both the multiplying fractions.

This can be demonstrated by folding a sheet of paper:

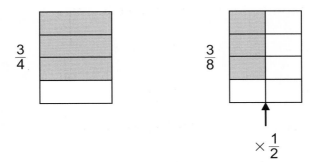

The answer, $\frac{3}{8}$ is smaller in size/value than either the $\frac{3}{4}$ or the $\frac{1}{2}$.

**Things to check #10. Mathematics vocabulary 'of'**

We say 'three quarters of 12' and '7% of £300'. If 'of' is used in this way in mathematics, then it means 'multiply'.

$$\frac{3}{4} \times 12 \quad and \quad \frac{7}{100} \times £300$$

**Practising multiplying by fractions**

a)  $\frac{2}{3} \times 9 =$          b)  $\frac{5}{7} \times 70 =$

c)  $\frac{4}{11} \times \frac{8}{9} =$          d)  $\frac{3}{2} \times \frac{5}{7} =$

e)  $12 \times \frac{3}{4} =$          f)  $\frac{2}{5} \times \frac{70}{111} =$

Answers:

f) $\frac{140}{555}$          e) 6          d) $\frac{15}{14}$

c) $\frac{32}{99}$          b) 50          a) 6

**Dividing by fractions**

Some logic may help to explain a process (and its outcome) that confuses many people.

When we **multiplied** a number by a fraction whose value was less than 1 the answer was smaller than the original number. Since division is the opposite of multiplication, we might reasonably expect an opposite result.

**When we divide a number by a fraction whose value is less than 1 the answer will be bigger than the original number.**

Once again, language and the basic fraction, a half, can help us understand before we get to the symbols.

'How many halves in one whole?' Commonsense and experience tell us the answer is 'two'.

'How many halves in one whole?' can also be phrased as 'what is 1 divided by a half?'

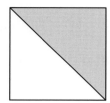 

If we extend the 'half' example to a third, 'how many thirds in one?' Again, commonsense tells us that there are 3.

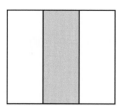

Then also, 'how many quarters in 1?' The answer is 4.

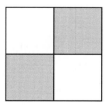

The pattern in symbols is, so far:

$$1 \div \frac{1}{2} = 2 \qquad 1 \div \frac{1}{3} = 3 \qquad 1 \div \frac{1}{4} = 4$$

1 divided by a half = 2    1 divided by a third = 3    1 divided by a quarter = 4

The pattern suggests that:

$$1 \div \frac{1}{5} = 5 \qquad 1 \div \frac{1}{6} = 6 \qquad 1 \div \frac{1}{7} = 7$$

The generalisation from these examples is:

**'Turn the dividing fraction upside down and multiply'**

For example:
$$1 \div \frac{1}{5} = 1 \times \frac{5}{1} = 5$$

Another example:
$$2 \div \frac{1}{5}$$

'How many fifths in 2?' The answer is going to be twice as many as 'how many fifths in 1?'

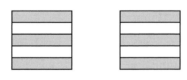

5 fifths    +    5 fifths    =    10 fifths    in    2

There are 5 fifths in 1 and thus there are 10 fifths in 2.

So the same rule applies again.

**'Turn the fraction upside down and multiply'.**   $2 \div \frac{1}{5} = 2 \times \frac{5}{1}$

It is almost as though the visible division sign and the division sign hidden in the fraction combine to make a multiplication.

**Numerators other than 1**

For example:
$$4 \div \frac{2}{3}$$

There are 3 thirds in 1, so there will be four times as many in 4. There are 12 thirds in 4, but since two thirds is twice the value of one third, then there should be half as many, that is 6 lots of two thirds in 4. The following diagram may help explain this:

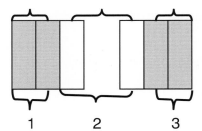 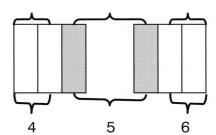

There are 12 thirds in the 4 squares above, but when they are grouped in twos, this reduces to 6 lots of 'two thirds'.

So, to work out $4 \div \frac{2}{3}$ first work out how many thirds in 4 by multiplying 4 by 3.

Then to work for two thirds, divide that answer by 2.

$$4 \times 3 = 12 \qquad\qquad 12 \div 2 = 6$$

This can be written as:
$$4 \times \frac{3}{2}$$

Again the procedure is, 'turn the multiplying fraction upside down and multiply.'

## Things to check #11

The 'turn the fraction upside down and multiply' rule can be explained mathematically in this way.

For a fraction divided by a fraction:

$$\frac{4}{5} \div \frac{2}{3}$$

The division can be re-written as a 'double' fraction:

$$\frac{\frac{4}{5}}{\frac{2}{3}}$$

This is too complicated to calculate, so we take the following steps.

To convert the bottom fraction, $\frac{2}{3}$ into 1, you multiply by the inverse of the fraction, that is you multiply by $\frac{3}{2}$.

To keep the value of the whole fraction the same, the top fraction $\frac{4}{5}$ must also be multiplied by the same inverse fraction $\frac{3}{2}$ (This is the same 'multiplying by 1' strategy we used for making equivalent fractions).

$$\frac{\frac{4}{5} \times \frac{3}{2}}{\frac{2}{3} \times \frac{3}{2}}$$

The bottom fraction $\frac{2}{3}$ has now become 1 and can be removed and we are left with:

$$\frac{4}{5} \times \frac{3}{2}$$

which is the 'turn upside down and multiply' rule.

## Practice

a) How many halves in four (wholes)?

b) How many thirds in six?     Check your answer at the bottom of the
                                page before you try Q3

c) How many tenths in ten?

d) How many $\frac{1}{5}$ in 2?

e) How many $\frac{2}{5}$ in 2?

f)  How many $\frac{2}{5}$ in 10?

g) What is $1 \div \frac{1}{10}$ ?     Check your answer at the bottom of the page
                                before you try Q8.

h) What is $3 \div \frac{1}{3}$ ?

i)  What is $\frac{4}{5} \div \frac{1}{5} =$

j)  What is $\frac{4}{5} \div \frac{2}{5} =$

k) What is $6 \div \frac{1}{10} =$

l)  What is $\frac{3}{10} \div \frac{9}{20} =$

Answers:

l) $\frac{2}{3}$     k) 60

j) 2     i) 5     h) 6     g) 100     f) 25

e) 5     d) 10     c) 10     b) 18     a) 8

**Improper fractions: top heavy fractions**

'Improper fractions' are fractions with the top number (numerator) bigger than the bottom number (denominator). They have, therefore, a value that is more than 1.

For example: $\dfrac{13}{5}$

To make this into a mixed number, use the hidden division sign.
In the example above, divide 13 by 5 answer 2 with 3 (fifths) left over.

$$\frac{13}{5} = 2\frac{3}{5}$$

A mixed number is made up of both a whole number and a fraction. To change a mixed number into an improper fraction you reverse this process.

For example:

To change $4\dfrac{3}{10}$ into a top heavy (improper) fraction:

Multiply 4 (the whole number) by 10 to convert it into tenths:

$$4 \times 10 = 40 \text{ tenths} = \frac{40}{10}$$

Add on the 3 tenths:

$$\frac{40}{10} + \frac{3}{10} = \frac{43}{10}$$

$$4\frac{3}{10} = \frac{43}{10}$$

## Practice

Convert these top heavy fractions to mixed numbers.

a) $\dfrac{21}{20}$  b) $\dfrac{52}{25}$

c) $\dfrac{7}{2}$  d) $\dfrac{10}{3}$

e) $\dfrac{17}{5}$  f) $\dfrac{103}{10}$

Answers:

a) $1\dfrac{1}{20}$  b) $2\dfrac{2}{25}$  c) $3\dfrac{1}{2}$

d) $3\dfrac{1}{3}$  e) $3\dfrac{2}{5}$  f) $10\dfrac{3}{10}$

## Proportion and ratio

Proportion and ratio have some similarities to fractions. They are about comparing quantities and about dividing things up.

For example, a mix for my favourite fruit pudding topping, crumble, is made from three ingredients in the ratio:

6 parts of flour : 3 parts of butter : 2 parts of sugar

$$6 : 3 : 2$$

So, in my crumble mix the total of parts is $6 + 3 + 2$ parts, that is 11 parts.

The parts could be written as fractions. The total of the fractions will be 1.

$\frac{6}{11}$ are flour, $\frac{3}{11}$ are butter, $\frac{2}{11}$ are sugar.

So, every 110g of crumble mix divides up (if that reversal were possible) into:

60g of flour, 30g of butter, 20g of sugar.

## Things to check #12

It seems that fractions use the line from the division symbol and proportion uses the dots.

$$\text{fraction} \quad \div \quad \frac{3}{4} \qquad\qquad \text{proportion} \quad : \quad 7:5$$

A second example of proportion.

In a mix for concrete the proportions are:

3 parts of sand: 2 parts of chippings: 1 part of cement

$$3:2:1$$

So there is a total of 3 + 2 + 1 parts, that is, a total of 6 parts

$\frac{3}{6}$ or $\frac{1}{2}$ are sand, $\qquad \frac{2}{6}$ or $\frac{1}{3}$ are chippings, $\qquad \frac{1}{6}$ is cement.

So, if I am mixing concrete I use 3 shovels of sand, 2 shovels of chippings and 1 shovel of cement.

Third example:

In a class, the ratio of girls to boys is 3:5. If there are 32 pupils in the class, how many girls are there?

There are 3 + 5 = 8 parts in the ratio, therefore, $\frac{3}{8}$ are girls, which can be written as:

$$\frac{3}{8} \times 32 = 12 \text{ pupils are girls}$$

## Practice

a) In a class the proportion of boys to girls is 4:5. If there are 36 pupils in the class, how many are girls?

b) A shade of paint is made in the ratio of 1 part of red, 2 parts of blue and 7 parts of white. If I need to make 1 litre of paint, how much blue paint do I need?

c) A concrete mix requires 3 parts of sand, 2 parts of chippings and 1 part of cement, how much sand do I need when making up 120 kg of concrete?

Answers:

a) 20    b) 0.2 Litres (20 cl)    c) 60 Kg

## Probability: part 1

When we try to guess the chances that something will happen, for example, that a football team will win its next match, we are estimating the **probability** of the win.

If it is likely that the team will win, we would guess a probability of close to 1. If we think the team has little chance of winning we would guess a probability of a win as close to zero. If we thought it was an even match then the probability would be close to $\frac{1}{2}$.

A more precise example, numerically, is the probability of a spinning coin landing to show heads or tails.

There are only two possible outcomes, heads or tails. The probability that the coin will land heads up is 1 out of 2. (The same probability applies to the coin landing tails up.)

When we know all the possible outcomes and the probability of each outcome, those probabilities will add up to 1.
In the coin example, $\frac{1}{2} = \frac{1}{2} = 1$.

A similar argument applies to throwing a six-sided die. The chance of getting a particular number, say 5 is 1 in 6, $\frac{1}{6}$.

We will return for a second look at probability after the section on percentages.

A probability is: $\dfrac{\text{the number of chances of winning}}{\text{the total of all the probabilities}}$

The closer this fraction is to 1, the better the chance of success. The closer this fraction is to zero, the more likely it will be failure.

The probability of winning the National Lottery Jackpot is $\frac{1}{14,000,000}$ one over fourteen million. The chances of winning the Jackpot are close to zero, but, since someone does win most weeks, not zero.

# Decimals

Decimals are closely related to fractions. Essentially decimals are fractions with special, limited value denominators.

The denominators are based on 10. They are tenths, hundredths, thousandths, etc.

$$0.1 \qquad \frac{1}{10}$$

$$0.01 \qquad \frac{1}{100}$$

$$0.001 \qquad \frac{1}{1000}$$

So 0.111 can be interpreted as $\frac{1}{10} + \frac{1}{100} + \frac{1}{1000}$

Because decimals use regular, consistent values for the denominators, the denominator is not used, it is implied. In essence the denominator is absorbed into place values.

We write     0.1     which has a value of one tenth.

We write     0.01     which has a value of one hundredth.

We write     0.001   which has a value of one thousandth.

In fact, decimals can be viewed as an extension of place value. Whole number place values are based on ten, hundred, thousand and so on. Decimal place values are based on tenth, hundredth and thousandth and so on. The unit is the central, key place value.

If we restrict ourselves to these values for the example below, then we can show how the 10x relationship is consistent.

2 2 2 2. 2 2 2

⟵ 10x

Each 2 is 10x bigger than the previous 2 in the direction shown by the arrow.

2 2 2 2. 2 2 2

⟶ ÷ 10

Each 2 is ÷ 10 smaller in the direction of the arrow.

## Things to check #13

A common mistake when writing the sequence of tenths is to forget about place value at the change over to units.

The writing starts well: 0.1, 0.2, 0.3, 0.4, 0.5, 0.6, 0.7, 0.8, 0.9......

What is the next number?  It is 1.0.
(After nine tenths comes ten tenths and ten tenths is 1.)
The common error is to write 0.10 ('zero point ten').

## An explanation of decimals

Money is a good real life illustration of how decimals work. The unit of currency in the UK is the pound sterling:  £1

We divide the pound, which is our unit, our 'one', into 100 pence, so each pence is worth one hundredth of a pound:

$$1p = £1 \div 100 \qquad 1p = \frac{£1}{100}$$

If we divide a pound by ten we get ten pence. So ten pence is one tenth of a pound:

$$10p = £1 \div 10 \qquad 10p = \frac{£1}{10}$$

So, if we want to write one pound and twenty-three pence as numbers, we write:

$$£1.23$$

The 1 represents £1   one unit,

the 2 represents 2 tenths,  $\frac{2}{10}$  of a pound and

the 3 represents 3 hundredths,  $\frac{3}{100}$  of a pound.

The almost imperceptible dot  .    the decimal point, tells us that we are about to meet fractions of a pound.

For example:                    £13.56

The Euro (€) is also divided into smaller value coins, the smallest of which is the cent (¢). The cent is one hundredth of a Euro.

The US dollar ($) is also divided into 100 cents.

**A second explanation of decimals**

There is a symmetry in decimal numbers. The symmetry doesn't centre on the decimal point.

It centres on the unit digit.

Numbers to the left of the unit digit represent values that are:

| | |
|---|---|
| Tens | 1 x 10 |
| Hundreds | 1 x 100 |
| Thousands | 1 x 1000    (and so on) |

This sequence is in the opposite direction when we write the numbers see below.

Numbers to the right of the unit digit and, therefore after the decimal point represent values that are 10 times, 100 times, 1000 times (and so on) smaller. That is, the numbers are:

| | |
|---|---|
| Tenths | $1 \times \frac{1}{10}$ |
| Hundredths | $1 \times \frac{1}{100}$ |
| Thousandths | $1 \times \frac{1}{1000}$    (and so on) |

For example

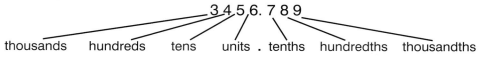

3 4 5 6 . 7 8 9

thousands    hundreds    tens    units . tenths    hundredths    thousandths

## Things to check #14. Why no unit-ths?

For whole numbers we have thousands, hundreds, tens and units. For decimal fractions we have tenths, hundredths and thousandths. There are no 'unit-ths'. The reason for this is explained above. The units are the focus, the base. Units are multiplied to make tens, hundreds, etc or divided to make tenths, hundredths, etc.

## Things to check #15. The sound of decimals

The words used for decimals end in 'ths' as in tenths, hundredths, thousandths and so on. The sound of 'ths' is very soft and people may not actually hear it. This means that they may not hear a difference between 'three hundreds' and 'three hundredths'.

This can lead to confusion and uncertainty. It will handicap any understanding of decimals and, therefore, any learner who appears to be struggling with decimals should be checked for this problem.

**Back to money**

We can use money to help explain how decimals work. Money only offers us tenths and hundredths (no thousandths and beyond), but the principles can be shown using these values.

The Euro and the Dollar are also divided by 100. The outcome for both is called a cent.

The word 'cent' on its own or as part of a word infers 100, as in **cent**ury or per**cent**age.

**Things to check #16. Understanding the values of decimals**

Some decimals can be mis-interpreted, for example:

0.29 is seen (wrongly) as bigger than 0.3

.078 is seen (wrongly) as bigger than 0.7

To avoid errors like these, you need to 'read' the actual place values of the digits that make up the decimal number. For example:

0.29 is two tenths and nine hundredths.
0.3 is three tenths (if it was written 0.30, the error would be less likely)

0.078 is 7 hundredths and 8 thousandths
0.7 is 7 tenths

Alternatively try multiplying the decimals by 100 or 1000:

$$0.29 \times 100 = 29 \qquad 0.3 \times 100 = 30$$

$$0.078 \times 1000 = 78 \qquad 0.7 \times 1000 = 700$$

The comparison is then much easier.

## Addition and subtraction of decimal numbers

When we add or subtract whole numbers, we line up the place values. For example 1075 + 293 is written in 'vertical' from as:

$$
\begin{array}{r}
1075 \\
+\ 293 \\
\hline
\end{array}
$$

We add units to units, tens to tens, hundreds to hundreds.

The same rule applies to decimal numbers. Money helps remind us of this rule. For example we should add £5.00 and 50p as:

$$
\begin{array}{r}
£5.00 \\
+\ .50 \\
\hline
£5.50 \checkmark
\end{array}
$$

**NOT** as

$$
\begin{array}{r}
5 \\
+\ 50 \\
\hline
55 \quad ✗
\end{array}
$$

Money reminds us to line up like with like. Often people use the decimal point as a focus for this. This strategy is OK as long as you don't forget that the unit digit is the true focus.

Examples:

| Add £5.99 and £12.99 | Subtract £5.75 from £20.00 |
|---|---|
| $\begin{array}{r} £\ 5.99 \\ +12.99 \\ \hline £18.98 \end{array}$ | $\begin{array}{r} £\ 20.00 \\ -\ \ 5.75 \\ \hline £14.25 \end{array}$ |

See 'What to do when you can't add and subtract' for addition and subtraction methods.

The actual methods used for addition and subtraction with decimals are just the same as used with whole numbers. The key issue is to line up the place values correctly.

As with whole numbers the key to success is to line up the place values, which, in the case of decimals, can be checked by ensuring that the decimal points are lined up.

## Things to check #17.  Tenths or hundredths?

Although money is a good way of explaining decimals, there is a slight disadvantage. The main unit of currency, the pound Sterling, (or the Euro or the US dollar), is divided into 100 pence or cents. When we write 50p, which is half of a pound, as decimal money we write it as £0.50, but when we write $\frac{1}{2}$ as a decimal in arithmetic we write 0.5.

The zero used at the end of 0.50 actually adds no more mathematical information than writing half as 0.5, but it is the custom when we write money.

Cheques in the US are often written as a fraction.
For example, $47\frac{36}{100}$ instead as $47.36.

## Multiplication with decimal numbers

There can be confusion over the basic concept of what the consequences are of multiplying decimal numbers.

First, it matters a lot whether the multiplying number is bigger or smaller than 1. There is a tendency for people to think (wrongly) that multiplication always makes things bigger. This is not so!

**Note:** When the multiplying number is less than 1, then the multiplied number is made smaller in value.

For example, if 0.5 is the multiplying number and 12 is the multiplied number:

$$0.5 \times 12 = 6$$

If we use words rather than just symbols, the answer makes sense:

0.5 is a half, and a half of 12 is 6, $\left( \frac{1}{2} \times 12 = \frac{12}{2} = 6 \right)$

Another example shows how this comes about. Again we can use the equivalence of decimals and fractions to help the explanation.

$$25 \times 0.2 = 5 \quad \left( 0.2 \text{ is two tenths,} \quad \frac{2}{10} \times 25 = \frac{50}{10} = 5 \right)$$

Multiplying by two tenths is done by multiplying by 2 and then dividing by 10.

Of course, the multiplying numbers (0.5 and 0.2) have been made bigger.

**Note:** If both the multiplying and the multiplied numbers are less than 1 then **both** become smaller.

For example:

$$0.5 \times 0.5 = 0.25$$

(a half times a half = a quarter)

$$0.1 \times 0.1 = 0.01$$

(a tenth times a tenth = a hundredth)

**Things to check #18**

There is a hidden division sign in fractions. There is also a hidden division in decimals. Actually, it is more a matter of 'being understood' than hidden. This can be explained by remembering that decimals are special fractions (they are sometimes called decimal fractions), so, for example:

$$\times\, 0.1 = \times\frac{1}{10} \qquad \times\, 0.2 = \times\frac{2}{10} \qquad \times\, 0.01 = \times\frac{1}{100}$$

The confusion is that:
multiplying by 0.1 is, in fact, dividing by 10 and
multiplying by 0.01 is, in fact, dividing by 100

**Things to check #19**

One of the **key skills** in all the '*What to do when you can't....*' books is the use of the question:

'Is the answer bigger or smaller?'

You have to choose one of the options and not give the literal answer 'Yes'!

The question acts as a first estimation of the answer and should reduce the chance of obtaining a 'silly' answer.

## Practice

In these questions you have to make a decision as to whether the answer is bigger or smaller. You should make that decision without doing the full calculation.

1.  15 x 0.2 = [   ]    Is the answer bigger than 15?    Yes / No
        Is the answer bigger than 0.2?    Yes / No

2.  3.5 x 10.8 = [   ]    Is the answer bigger than 3.5?    Yes / No
        Is the answer bigger than 10.8?    Yes / No

3.  0.04 x 555 = [   ]    Is the answer bigger than 555?    Yes / No
        Is the answer bigger than 0.04?    Yes / No

4.  0.6 x 0.04 = [   ]    Is the answer bigger than 0.6?    Yes / No
        Is the answer bigger than 0.04?    Yes / No

## A rule to use when multiplying decimals

Following on from the sections above, we can look at the pattern when we multiply a decimal number by another decimal number. This pattern helps us decide on how many decimal places there are in the new number (the product).

**A product is the answer you get when you multiply two numbers together.**

**A decimal place is the number of digits after the decimal point, the number of decimal digits.**

**The rule is:**

Count the number of decimal places in the multiplying numbers (for example in 3.47 x 8.1, there are three decimal numbers, or digits, 4, 7 and 1). So three will be the number of decimal places in the answer. (In our example the answer is 28.107. The three decimal digits are 1, 0 and 7).

72

**The explanation is:**

There are 'hidden' denominators in decimals:

For example,

$$1.2 \times 0.6 = 0.72$$

$$\frac{12}{10} \times \frac{6}{10} = \frac{72}{100}$$

and another example,

$$0.204 \times 0.3 = 0.612$$

$$\frac{204}{100} \times \frac{3}{10} = \frac{612}{1000}$$

and a third example,

$$4.53 \times 0.04 = 0.1812$$

$$\frac{453}{100} \times \frac{4}{100} = \frac{1812}{10000}$$

**Things to check #20.  Decimal places**

Be careful when zeros are involved in decimal places. For example, 0.50 counts as 1 decimal place, but 0.05 counts as 2 decimal places. The 0 in 0.50 can be removed to leave 0.5 with no impact on the value of the decimal. If the 0 is written, the decimal is 5 tenths and no hundredths. Without the zero it is still 5 tenths. If we got enthusiastic about useless zeros we could make it 0.500, which would be 5 tenths, no hundredths and no thousandths, but it is still 5 tenths.

However, 0.05 is 5 hundredths. If we removed the 0 it would become 0.5, which is no longer 5 hundredths, but becomes 5 tenths.

## Practice

For the questions below you have to decide how many decimal places in the answer before you do the calculation. (You can use a calculator to do the calculations and check your answers).

How many decimal places in each answer?

a)  4.5 x 3.3          _____ decimal places

b)  2.02 x 7.9         _____ decimal places

c)  6.6 x 5.4          _____ decimal places

d)  0.67 x 0.14        _____ decimal places

e)  0.40 x 4.6         _____ decimal places

Answers:

a) 2 decimal places   b) 3 dp   c) 2 dp   d) 4 dp   e) 2 dp

## Practice

Calculate the answers with paper and pen, then check with a calculator.

a)   36 x 0.2 =          b)   0.4 x 0.02 =

(check your answers to these questions before moving on to question 3 and beyond)

c)   0.002 x 44 =          d)   50 x 0.43 =

e)   0.62 x 5 =          f)   3.5 x 4.2 =

g)   1.05 x 6.21 =          h)   100.1 x 0.02 =

i)   11.001 x 0.03 =          j)   500 x 0.0001 =

Answers:

g) 6.5205          h) 2.002          i) 0.33003          j) 0.05

c) 0.088          d) 21.5          e) 3.1          f) 14.7

a) 7.2          b) 0.008

## Things to check #21.  Measuring

When I buy a bottle of wine it contains 75cl (cl is centi-litres). When my daughter buys a can of cola it contains 330ml (ml is milli-litres).

The metric system of quantities uses 'centi' and 'milli' to deal with quantities less then 1 unit. For example, timber dimensions at my local DIY store are usually given in mm, milli-metres.

This system of pre-fixes avoids the use of decimals.

The pre-fix 'centi' means hundredths $\frac{1}{100}$ and the pre-fix 'milli' means thousandths $\frac{1}{1000}$.

So my 75cl bottle of wine contains $\frac{75}{100}$ or $\frac{3}{4}$ of a litre of wine  or 0.75 litres,

and Sarah's 330ml cola contains $\frac{330}{1000}$ or close to $\frac{1}{3}$ of a litre of cola   or 0.33 litres.

There is a variation on this theme with grams and kilograms. The pre-fix 'kilo' means 1000x, so a kilogram is 1000 grams which means that a gram is one thousandth $\frac{1}{1000}$ of a kilogram.

To change grams into kilograms, we have to divide the gram value by 1000.

For example:

a 500g bag of apples contains $\frac{500}{1000}$ or $\frac{1}{2}$ a kilogram of apples.

**Practice these examples:**

a)   Write 50 cm as a fraction of a metre.          _____

b)   Write 25 cl as a fraction of a litre.          _____

c)   Write 25 ml as a fraction of a litre.          _____

d)   Write 455 mm as a decimal of a metre.          _____

e)   Write 450 ml as a decimal.          _____

f)   Write 0.6 m in mm.          _____

g)   Write 1/4 m in cm.          _____

h)   Write 1/2 litre in ml.          _____

Answers:

h) 500 ml          g) 25 cm          f) 600 mm          e) 0.450
d) 0.455          c) 0.025          b) 0.25          a) 0.5

# Percentages

We meet percentages often in everyday life, much more than we meet fractions. Percentages are easier to understand than fractions which may well be why they were invented.

Percentages have been used since the fifteenth century with businessmen writing '30 p 100' to represent 30 out of 100 meaning 30% and 'X p cento' to mean 10%.

In ancient Roman times a $\frac{1}{100}$ tax (1%) was levied on all proceeds of sales by auction. The first example of the symbol $\overset{0}{\div}\overset{}{_0}$ appeared in 1425.

**Things to check #22.  Per thousand**

There is a per millage which means per thousand, using the symbol 'per M' and also the symbol $^0\!/\!_{00}$.

## What does the word 'percentage' mean?

'Per' means divide.  'Cent' means 100.  Percentages are fractions with the denominator, the name, the dividing number, as 100. The 100 is hidden or inferred in the symbol $\%$. Percent means dividing by 100.

As this way of writing percentages is always the case, and as 'percent' tells you that you divided by 100, a percentage is written, not as a fraction.

For example:

$$\frac{15}{100} \quad \text{but as} \quad 15\%$$

So 15% is a way of writing the fraction $\quad \frac{15}{100}$

The symbol % could be interpreted as a 'divide sign and the two zeros from 100'

$$\div \ \frac{0}{0}$$

## Things to check #23.  The hidden information in %

Once again there is some hidden information. The percent symbol % hides the instruction to divide by 100.

So 36% translates as $\quad \frac{36}{100} \quad 36 \div 100$

## A big advantage for percentages

Percentages have some advantages over fractions, which is good news, otherwise we would be working on a new variation of the fraction theme for little benefit. The benefits include easier comparisons of different values.

Different percentages are easier to compare than different fractions, for example, comparing $\frac{23}{48}$ and $\frac{35}{72}$ is more challenging than comparing 47.9% and 48.6%.

Bank interest rates may sometimes be changed by 0.25% (often said as 'a quarter of a point'), which is easier for people to appraise than a change of $\frac{1}{400}$.

Percentages (the easier values) are more common in everyday usage, for example, we might be asked in a restaurant to tip 12.5%, but would be less likely to be asked to tip $\frac{1}{8}$ (though this might be easier to calculate).

Most of us have an understanding of the numbers from 1 to 100, so, when borrowing money, it is easy to compare interest rates of, for example, 7.5% and 7.7%.

## How to calculate some key value percentages

Most of the key percentage values are calculated by division, which reminds us that percentages are a variation of fractions, *see page 4.*

50%     divide by 2, ($\frac{1}{2}$)

for example, 50% of £410 is £410 ÷ 2 = £205

25%     divide by 2 and then divide by 2 again ($\frac{1}{4}$)

for example, 25% of £92 is £92 ÷ 2 = £46, then £46 ÷ 2 = £23

12.5%   divide by 2, divide by 2 again and then divide by 2 for a third time ($\frac{1}{8}$).

for example, 12.5% of £104 is

£104 ÷ 2 = £52, then £52 ÷ 2 = £26, then  £26 ÷ 2 = £13

The fraction sequence for 50%, 25% and 12.5% is    $\frac{1}{2}, \frac{1}{4}, \frac{1}{8}$.

10%     divide by 10 (1/10)

for example, 10% of £91 is  £91 ÷ 10 = £9.10

5%      divide by 10, then divide by 2 ($\frac{1}{20}$)

for example, 5% of £66 is £66 ÷ 10 = £6.60, then £6.60 ÷ 2 = £3.30

2.5%    divide by 10, then divide by 2, then divide by 2 again ($\frac{1}{40}$)

for example, 2.5% of £66 is £66 ÷ 10  = £6.60, then £6.60 ÷ 2 = £3.30, then £3.30 ÷ 2 = £1.65

20%    divide by 10, then multiply by 2 ($\frac{2}{10}$ or $\frac{1}{5}$)

for example, 20% of £32 is £32 ÷ 10 = £3.20,
then £3.20 x 2 = £6.40

1%    divide by 100 ($\frac{1}{100}$)

for example, 1% of £26 is £26 ÷ 100 = £0.26

2%    divide by 100, then multiply by 2 ($\frac{2}{100}$ or $\frac{1}{50}$)

for example, 2% of £26 is £26 ÷ 100 = £0.26,
then £0.26 x 2 = £0.52

These key values are sufficient for many estimates of percentages. They can be combined to give several more values, for example, in early 2008, the Value Added Tax in the UK was 17.5%.

17.5% can be calculated from 10% + 5% + 2.5% (5% is half of 10% and 2.5% is half of 5%).

Other combinations include:

75%  =  50% + 25%

90%  = 100% - 10%

60%  =  50% + 10%

15%  =  10% + 5%

9%  =  10% - 1%

## Key percentage values

The key values calculated above are shown on this 0 – 100% line. They span most of the line.

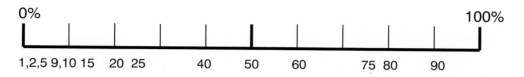

## Things to check #24

One of the fundamental ideas that runs through the 'What to do...' books is the idea of maximising the use of key numbers (1, 2, 5, 10, 20, 50 etc.) by combining them to access other values. The section above illustrates how this works for percentages.

**Using a set procedure for calculating a percentage of a number**

A typical basic question might be:

'Calculate 30% of £550'

This calculation can be changed into a formula.

The symbols and words need to be interpreted first.

'of' means multiply

30% means $\frac{30}{100}$ which means we have to multiply by 30 and then divide by 100.

So: $\frac{30}{100} \times 550 = £165$

In order to make this particular calculation less complicated you can re-organise the numbers:

$$30 = 3 \times 10 \qquad\qquad 550 = 55 \times 10$$

$$\frac{30}{100} \times 550 = 3 \times 55 \times 10 \times 10 \;=\; \frac{3}{100} \times 55 \times 100$$

then the hundred from the original percentage, 30% or $\frac{30}{100}$ , and the hundred from 3 x 55 x 100 can be cancelled.

**Note:** You could have done this problem by using the key values of 20% and 10%, but the problem was explained to illustrate a method that works for all similar calculations. However, sometimes it is good to have an alternative method, maybe because you find the alternative better for you or maybe to check your answer.

## Practice

Sam earns £445 a week. If Sam is given a pay rise of 2%, how much extra does she earn per week?

$$\frac{2}{100} \times 445 = \frac{890}{100} = £8.90$$

## Things to check #25. Language and vocabulary

Even the simplest number statement can be made confusing in 'word problems'. For example:

$$\frac{15}{75} = \boxed{\phantom{0}}\%$$

What is 15 out of 75 as a percentage?

Write $\frac{15}{75}$ as a percentage.               WHAT   FIND   HOW MUCH

What percentage of 75 is 15?                              ?????????????

Find what percentage of 75 is 15.

How many percent of 75 is 15?

Fifteen out of seventy-five people at a meeting drink coffee for their break. What percentage of people drink coffee?

60 out of 75 people on a bus are seated. The rest are standing. What percentage of people are standing?

**Things to check #26.  Algebra can help with formulas**

Although algebra can create anxiety in many people, it has some really useful applications. It can help us understand generalisations by providing a formula that will work for all similar examples, whatever the numbers involved.

For these percentage questions, which follow a pattern of 'a percentage times a value' we can use the shorthand of algebra to create a formula.

If we represent the percentage by p, and the number we are applying the percentage to as V, then the formula is:

$$p\% \text{ of } V \quad \text{which becomes} \quad \frac{p}{100} \times V$$

In a question such as, 'find 3% of 7200', p is 3 and V is 7200.

$$\frac{3}{100} \times 7200 = 216$$

In the example, 'find 17% of £200', p is 17 and V is £200.

$$\frac{17}{100} \times £200 = £34$$

In the example, 'if 23% of 5000 tea drinkers preferred Earl Black's tea, how many people was that?'

$$p \text{ is } 23\% \text{ and } V \text{ is } 5000$$

$$\frac{23}{1000} \times 5000 = 1150$$

## Percentages above 100%

When football managers talk about 'the lads' making a big effort in the match, they sometimes say 'I'm looking for 110% effort.'

Percentages can be greater than 100% (more realistically than the football manager example).

For example, if a car costs £5000 and its price is increased by 4%, then the new price will be 104% of £5000.

Using our formula, $\frac{p}{100} \times V$

$$p \text{ is } 100 + 4 = 104\% \text{ and } V \text{ is } £5000$$

so the new price is:

$$\frac{104}{100} \times £5000 = £5200$$

An alternate method is to calculate the percentage increase and add it to the original price.

A 4% increase can be calculated using our formula $\frac{p}{100} \times V$

$$p \text{ is } 4\% \quad \text{and} \quad V = £5000$$

The increase in price is $\frac{4}{100} \times £5000 = £200$,

so the new price is $£5000 + £200 = £5200$

200% would be twice the original amount,

300% would be three times the original amount, and so on.

At one stage in 2009 inflation in Zimbabwe was over 10,000,000%.

## Practice

Try questions 1 and 2 first and check that your answers are correct before moving to the next examples.

a) What is 110% of £300?

b) A car costing £4000 last year is now 5% more expensive. What is the new price of the car?

c) What is 120% of £500?

d) If the price of a £800 sofa is increased by 10%, what is the new price?

e) If the price of a £440 table is increased by 2%, what is the new price?

f) The train fare from Bristol to London is £140. If fares increase by 3.5%, what is the new fare?

Answers:

a) £330        c) £600

b) £4200       d) £880        e) £448.80        f) £144.90

## Two ways to work out percentage discounts

If there is a sale and everything is labelled as '20% OFF', then there are two ways to get the new price.

For example: a jacket is priced at £142 before the sale. What is the new price with the 20% reduction?

### Method 1.
Calculate the discount and subtract it from the original price.

Discount:    20% of £142

$$\frac{20}{100} \times £142 = £28.40$$

**Note:** 20% of £142 could also be calculated by working out 10%, £14.20 and doubling £28.40

Subtract the discount from the original price:

$$£142.00 - £28.40 = £113.60$$

### Method 2.
Take away the percentage discount from 100% and use this percentage to work out the new price.

Sale percentage:         $100\% - 20\% = 80\%$

Calculate the new price:      80% of £142

$$\frac{80}{100} \times £142 = £113.60$$

One of the factors which might influence your choice of method is the numbers involved. Method 1 used 20% which is an easy multiplication. Method 2 used 80% which is a harder multiplication. It is usually a good idea to take a good look at a problem rather than rushing in with the first idea that comes to mind.

## Calculating a percentage from two numbers

This type of question involves calculating what percentage one quantity or number is of another quantity or number.

First example:

> 34 out of 85 pupils at a school said they preferred skimmed milk to full fat milk. What percentage of pupils prefer skimmed milk?

The answer is calculated in three steps:

1. Create a fraction.

2. Make it a decimal by dividing.

3. Convert it to a percentage by multiplying by 100.

The sequence of steps is:-

**Fraction >>> Decimal >>> Percentage**

First step:       make a fraction,   $\frac{34}{85}$

Second step:   make it a decimal by dividing     $34 \div 85 = 0.4$

Third step:      make it a percentage by multiplying by 100
$0.4 \times 100 = 40\%$

Second example:

A student scores 54 out of a possible 75 marks in a science examination. What is his percentage score?

First step:          make a fraction,          $\dfrac{54}{75}$

Second step:     make it a decimal by dividing,          $54 \div 75 = 0.72$

Third step:        make it a percentage by multiplying by 100,
                        $0.72 \times 100 = 72\%$

**Things to check #27. Calculating an original value when you know the percentage change**

In this type of calculation, all three versions of dealing with values of less than one, fractions, decimals and percentages are used.

In these problems you have to work back from an increased or reduced percentage to 100% (the original value).

A typical problem is:

A car's price is increased by 5% to £8610. What was its original price?

In terms of percentage:

The original price is 100%
The new price is 105%
The original price is lower than £8500

$$8610 \div 105 \times 100 = \frac{8610}{105} \times 100 = £8200$$

A good check on whether you have the two percentages in the correct places is to ask, *'Is the original price lower or higher than the given value?'*

In this problem, the original price is lower. Dividing by 105 and then multiplying by 100 will lead to a lower value answer.

A typical problem where the original value is higher:

A jacket costs £56 in a '20% off' sale. What was the original price?

The original price is 100%
The new price is 80%     (100% - 20%)
The original price is higher than £56

$$56 \div 80 \times 100 \qquad \frac{56}{80} \times 100 = £70.00$$

Rough check:   The original price is £70, which is higher than the sale price.

## Visualising and estimating percentages

There are levels of 'closeness of estimate' that you can choose to achieve by visualising percentages. One of the benefits of using percentages rather than fractions is that percentages are easier to compare. For example:

In a sale, '50% off' is obviously a better deal than '20% off'.

For a pay rise, 4.5% is a better increase than 4.3%.

If you visualise 100% as a 10 x 10 square:

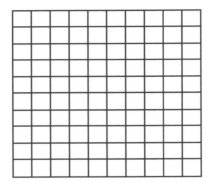

Then 50% is half of the square    and    20% is 2 tenths of the square.

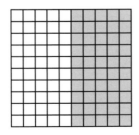

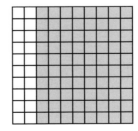

50%                                           20%

One of the benefits of this visualisation is that it gives a sense of what 20% is in proportion to 100% and 50%.

In a sale 20% off is not bad, but the visualisation shows it is not earth shatteringly good nor is it as good as 50% off.

In terms of the rate of interest some shops charge for their loans, the visualisation may make you realistically cautious. Often these rates are close to 30%, which looks like (again using 50% for comparison purposes):

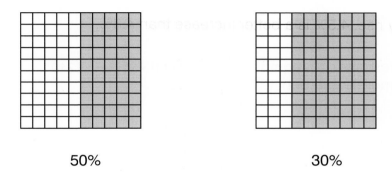

50%                                 30%

30% is close to one third, which, very crudely and approximately, means that if you borrow £500 and pay nothing back, in 3 years you will owe £1000.

## Things to check #28.  Monthly and Annual interest rates

Is 2% interest per month for twelve months the same deal as 24% per one year?

Start with 24% interest per annum on a £1000 loan.

If we use our $\frac{p}{100} \times V$ formula:

The interest after 12 months is:          $£1000 \times \frac{24}{100} = £240$
after 12 months the debt is £1240

If we use the formula for 1%          $£1000 \times \frac{2}{100} = £20$
after 1 month the debt is £1020

By the second month:          $£1020 \times \frac{2}{100} = £20.40$
the debt is £1040.40

and by the third month:          $£1040.40 \times \frac{2}{100} = £20.81$
the debt is  £1061.21

and so on for 12 months to give a final debt of £1268.24, which has increased the debt by £268.24 an annual interest rate of 26.8%.

## Probability: part 2

Sometimes weather forecasts use percentages to express the chance or probability that it will rain (or snow). A 90% chance of rain means that rain is more likely than when the chance is given as 20%.

If we think something is just as likely to go either way of two possibilities we sometimes say the chances are 'fifty fifty.' We mean 50% chance of success and 50% chance of failure.

The percentages used are from 100% which means absolutely certain to 0% which means absolutely impossible.

## Mix and Match Cards

Photocopy these onto card and cut them out.

They can be used to practise key facts and relationships.

Matching:
Cards have to be matched for value, for example,   0.5 and 1/2

Mixing:
Cards have to be combined to make a target value, for example,  75% has to be 'mixed and matched', possibly by using a 25% and a 50% card or by mixing a 50% and $\frac{1}{4}$ card.

The operation cards (x + ÷ −) can be used to make more challenging mixes.

50%

0.5

25%

1/2

10%

0.1

75%

3/4

0.50

1/4

10%

5%

0.1

0.01

10%

5%

15%

1/10

1/100

0.01

0.50

1.0

1/20

1/50

2%

1/5

20%

60%

+

X

90%

40%

—

80%

0.9

0.8

÷

9/10

8/10

4/5

0.4

0.6

**Blank cards to use to add your own values to the selection**

## 100 squares for demonstrating percentages